D1535339

WATCH
ME

THE WOODLAND FROLICS SERIES

Who Are You?

Watch Me

Downy Duck Grows Up

Little Lost BoBo

Chippy Chipmunk's Vacation

Gordo and the Hidden Treasure

Chichi's Magic

The Heart of the Wild

WATCH ME

by Adda Mai Sharp
and
Epsie Young

Illustrated by
Elizabeth Rice

STECK-VAUGHN COMPANY
AUSTIN, TEXAS

THE STORIES IN THIS BOOK

Watch Me!

Watch me!
Up I go!

Up I go!
Watch me!

Watch me climb!
Watch me!
I am Cubby Bear!
Watch me!

8

Down I come.
Down, down, down!

Up I go again.
Up, up, up!
Watch me!

Where Is Cubby Bear?

"Where is Cubby Bear?
I can not see him,"
said Skippy Rabbit.
"Where can he be?"

10

Skippy Rabbit called,
"Cubby Bear! Cubby Bear!
Where are you, Cubby Bear?
I can not see you.
Where are you?"

See Me?

Cubby Bear looked down.
He called, "Here I am!
See me?
I am in a hole.
I am in a hole in the tree.
See me in the hole?"

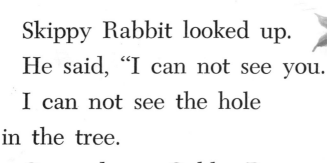

Skippy Rabbit looked up.
He said, "I can not see you.
I can not see the hole
in the tree.
Come down, Cubby Bear.
Come down and play."

Cubby Bear called again,
"Look, Skippy Rabbit.
Look in the tree.
I am in a hole in the tree.
Here I am!
See me?"

Skippy Rabbit said,
"I will not look.
I want to play."

Then he called,
"Cubby Bear! Cubby Bear!
Come down and play.
Come down, Cubby Bear!
Come down and play!"

Yum-Yum-Yum!

Cubby Bear said,
"I will not come down.
I smell something.
I smell something good.
It is in this hole."

Cubby Bear sniffed.
He sniffed again.
"Skippy Rabbit," he called,
"I smell honey.
I smell honey in this hole.
It smells good.
Yum-yum-yum!
It smells good!"

Cubby Bear said, "Yum-yum-yum!
I smell honey.
Yum-yum-yum!
I like honey.
Yum-yum-yum!
I will look for honey!"

Skippy Rabbit sniffed.
He wiggled his nose.
He called,
"I can not smell honey.
Come down, Cubby Bear!
Come down and play."

19

Help! Help!

"Oh, oh, oh!" cried Cubby Bear.
"Oh, oh, oh!
Help! Help!
Help me, Skippy Rabbit!
Help me!"

And down the tree he came!

Downy Duck and Rusty Turtle
heard Cubby Bear.

They heard him cry,
"Help! Help!

Help me, Skippy Rabbit!

Help me!"

Away Downy Duck hurried
to help Cubby Bear.
Away Rusty Turtle hurried
to help him.

What did they see?

"Ha, ha, ha!"
laughed Downy Duck.

"Ha, ha, ha!"
laughed Rusty Turtle.

"Ha, ha, ha!"
laughed Skippy Rabbit.

"Oh, oh, oh!" cried Cubby Bear.
"My nose, my nose!
Oh, oh, oh!"

Skippy Rabbit laughed and
said,

"Up, up, up went Cubby Bear.
Down, down, down came he.
He went to look for honey.
But he found a honeybee!

He went to look for honey.
But he found a honeybee!"

"Look! A bee! A bee!"
cried Downy Duck.

"Look, Skippy Rabbit, look!"

But Skippy Rabbit did not look.
He laughed and said again,

"Up, up, up went Cubby Bear!
Down, down, down came he.
He went to look for honey.
But he found a honeybee!"

"Skippy Rabbit, do you hear
me?" cried Downy Duck.

"I said, 'A bee! A bee!' "

Where Is the Bee?

Skippy Rabbit said,
"The bee is in the honey.
  The honey is in the hole.
  And the hole is in the tree."

"But the bee is not in the honey.
The bee is down here!"
said Downy Duck.

"Down here!" cried Skippy Rabbit.
"Oh me! Oh my! Where is it?"

"Buzz-z-z!" said the bee.

"Here it is!" cried Downy Duck.
"Here it is! Look! Look!"

"Buzz-z-z!" said the bee again.

"Go away, bee, go away!"
cried Skippy Rabbit.
"I do not like you!"

"Buzz-z-z!" said the bee.
Then up and away it went.

"Watch the bee! Watch the bee!"
called Rusty Turtle.

Skippy Rabbit heard Rusty Turtle.
He looked up and down.
He did not see the honeybee.
He said, "The bee went
up and away, Rusty Turtle."

"The bee did go up and away,"
said Rusty Turtle.
"But it came down again.
Here it is! Here it is!
Watch it, Skippy Rabbit,
watch it!"

"Buzz-z-z!" said the bee.

"I can hear it, but
I can not see it,"
said Skippy Rabbit.
"Where can it be?"

"Buzz-z-z!" said the bee.

"Oh, it wants my nose!
What will I do?"
cried Skippy Rabbit.
"Help! Help!
Help me, Downy Duck!
Help me, Rusty Turtle!"

Rusty Turtle hurried
to Skippy Rabbit.
"Hide! Hide!" he cried.

Downy Duck ran to him
and said, "I'll help you.
Do not cry and do not hide.
I'll eat the honeybee.
Watch me! Watch me!"

But the bee said, "Buzz-z-z!"
Then up and away it went.

"Ha, ha, ha!"
laughed Rusty Turtle.

"Ha, ha, ha!"
laughed Downy Duck.

Then, "Ha, ha, ha!"
laughed Skippy Rabbit.

Eating

Downy Duck was eating berries.
Rusty Turtle was eating berries.
Skippy Rabbit was eating grass.

Downy Duck said,
"I like berries.
I like worms, too.
Do you like worms,
Skippy Rabbit?"

35

Skippy Rabbit said,
"I do not like worms.
I like grass.
Yum-yum-yum!
This is good grass!"

"I like grass, too,"
said Downy Duck.

"But I do not want grass now.
I do not want berries now.
I want a worm.
I want a big, fat worm."

Away he hurried to look
for a big, fat worm.

A Big, Fat Worm

"Here is a hole,"
called Rusty Turtle.

Downy Duck hurried to see
the hole.

"I see a worm in the hole!"
cried Downy Duck.
"It is a big, fat worm!"

"Watch me!" called Downy Duck.
"Watch me, Skippy Rabbit!
Watch me, Rusty Turtle!
Watch me eat this worm!"

Downy Duck pulled at the worm.
He pulled and he pulled
and he pulled.
Then over he went!

"Ha, ha, ha!"
laughed Skippy Rabbit.

"Ha, ha, ha!"
laughed Rusty Turtle.

Downy Duck did not laugh.

Downy Duck ate the worm.
Then he laughed, too.

"Yum-yum-yum!" he said.
"What a good worm!"

A Cry-Baby

Cubby Bear was not happy.
His nose hurt.
He wanted to play
with Skippy Rabbit.
He wanted to play
with Downy Duck and
Rusty Turtle.
He cried and cried.

"Hello, Cry-baby!"

Cubby Bear did not look up.
He said, "I am not a cry-baby!"

And then he cried again.

"Hello, Cry-baby!"

Cubby Bear looked up.
He looked here and there.
He looked up and down.
Then he saw Frisky Squirrel
in the tree.

Frisky Squirrel said,
"Hello, Cry-baby!
Hello, hello, hello!"

Cubby Bear said,
"I am not happy.
My nose hurts.
Skippy Rabbit laughed at me.
Downy Duck laughed at me.
Rusty Turtle laughed at me.
Oh, oh, oh! I am not happy!"

Then he cried again.
He just cried and cried.

"Oh, do not be a cry-baby,"
said Frisky Squirrel.

"Watch me! I am happy!
See me run and jump.
Watch me climb this tree.
Now watch me run down.
Oh, this is fun!
Come and play!
Come and play with me!"

And Cubby Bear did.
He said, "Now I am happy!
I just wanted to play!"

Who Wants a Picnic?

"A picnic, a picnic!
Who wants a picnic?
A picnic, a picnic!
Who wants a picnic?"

Downy Duck was in the woods.
He was singing.
He was singing,

"A picnic, a picnic!
Who wants a picnic?"

Frisky Squirrel was in the woods.
He heard Downy Duck singing,

"A picnic, a picnic!
Who wants a picnic?"

Frisky Squirrel cried, "I do!
I want a picnic!"

Downy Duck said,
"Then come with me."

51

Frisky Squirrel went
with Downy Duck.

Downy Duck went on singing,

"A picnic, a picnic!
Who wants a picnic?
A picnic, a picnic!
Who wants a picnic?"

Cubby Bear and Rusty Turtle
were in the woods.

They heard Downy Duck singing,

"A picnic, a picnic!
Who wants a picnic?"

Cubby Bear said, "I do!
I want a picnic!"

Rusty Turtle said, "I do!
I want a picnic!"

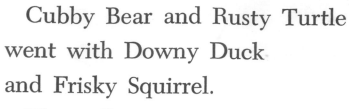

Cubby Bear and Rusty Turtle
went with Downy Duck
and Frisky Squirrel.
They all went on singing,

"A picnic, a picnic!
Who wants a picnic?"

54

Skippy Rabbit was in the woods.

He heard Downy Duck and
Cubby Bear.

He heard Rusty Turtle and
Frisky Squirrel.

He heard them singing,

"A picnic, a picnic!
Who wants a picnic?"

"A picnic?" cried Skippy Rabbit.
"Oh, I want a picnic!
A picnic is fun!
Let's have a picnic!"

55

What Will We Bring?

Downy Duck stopped singing.
Cubby Bear, Frisky Squirrel,
and Rusty Turtle stopped singing.

Downy Duck asked,
"What will we bring
to the picnic?

What will you bring,
Rusty Turtle?

What will you bring,
Frisky Squirrel?

What will you bring,
Skippy Rabbit?"

Rusty Turtle said,
"I'll bring some berries."

Frisky Squirrel said,
"I'll bring some nuts."

Skippy Rabbit said,
"I'll bring some grass."

Downy Duck said,
"I'll bring some big, fat worms.
What will you bring,
Cubby Bear?"

Cubby Bear said,
"I'll not bring honey!"

Then they laughed and laughed.

Skippy Rabbit said,
"He went to look for honey.
But he found a honeybee!"

The Picnic

The picnic was in the woods.
A big leaf was the tablecloth.
Downy Duck brought the worms.
Rusty Turtle and Cubby Bear
brought the berries.
Skippy Rabbit brought the grass.
Frisky Squirrel brought the nuts.

"Let's eat!" said Skippy Rabbit.

"Yes, let's eat!" they all said.

"I'll crack the nuts,"
said Frisky Squirrel.
"Watch me!
Watch me crack this nut!"

Crack! Crack! Crack!

"Look!" cried Skippy Rabbit.
"Look at Frisky Squirrel!

Frisky Squirrel is sitting
on the tablecloth!"

Frisky Squirrel ran up
into the tree.

"Ha, ha, ha!" he laughed.
"Watch me! Watch me!
Watch me crack this nut!
I was sitting on the tablecloth.
Now, I am sitting in the tree!"

Then they laughed and laughed.
"What fun! What fun!"
they all said.

The picnic was fun.

They ate and ate and ate.

Frisky Squirrel ate the nuts.

Rusty Turtle and Cubby Bear
ate the berries.

Downy Duck ate the worms.
He ate some berries
and some grass, too.

Skippy Rabbit ate some grass.
He ate some berries.
And then—
He ate the tablecloth!

Frisky Squirrel looked down
from the tree.

"Oh, look, look!" he cried.

"Skippy Rabbit is eating
the tablecloth!

Skippy Rabbit is eating
the tablecloth!"

They all laughed and laughed.

"I ate the tablecloth,"
said Skippy Rabbit.
"It was good, too!"

In and Out

"I am still hungry.
I want more berries,"
said Rusty Turtle.

"What! More berries!"
cried Frisky Squirrel.

"What! More berries!"
cried Skippy Rabbit.

"Yes," said Rusty Turtle.
"I am still hungry.
I did not eat a tablecloth."

Away he went to look
for more berries.

Rusty Turtle found more berries.
"Just watch me!" he called.
"Watch me eat these berries.
I can eat these and more, too.
Yum-yum-yum!
I like berries!"

By and by Rusty Turtle
stopped eating.
"Now watch me go to sleep,"
he said.

He pulled in his head.
He pulled in his feet.
His head popped out.

He pulled in his head.
His feet popped out.

He pulled in his feet again.
And again his head popped out.

Skippy Rabbit jumped
up and down.
"Look!" he shouted.
"Look at Rusty Turtle!"

"Ha, ha, ha,"
laughed Skippy Rabbit.

"I ate the tablecloth.
But I can still hop.
You ate more berries.
Now, in and out you pop!"

What Will We Do?

"Now, what will we do?"
asked Downy Duck.

"Let's go for a swim,"
said Rusty Turtle.

"No, no, no!" said Skippy Rabbit.
"No, no, no!" said Frisky Squirrel.
"No, no, no!" said Cubby Bear.

"Let's run and jump,"
said Skippy Rabbit.

"Oh, yes! Let's run and jump,"
said Frisky Squirrel.

"No, no, no!" said Rusty Turtle.
"No, no, no!" said Downy Duck.
"No, no, no!" said Cubby Bear.

"Then what will we do?"
asked Skippy Rabbit.

77

"I know what I am going to do.
I am going to swim,"
said Rusty Turtle.

Splash, splash!
Into the water he went.

Downy Duck said,
"I know what I am going to do.
I am going to swim."

Splash, splash!
Into the water he went.

"I know what I am going to do,"
said Skippy Rabbit.

"I am going to jump.
I like to jump over a big log."

Frisky Squirrel said,
"I am going to run.
I am going to run on this log."

I Am Not

Cubby Bear did not want to run.
He did not want to jump.
He did not want to swim.

"Watch me!" cried Frisky Squirrel.
"Watch me run on this log."

"Watch me!" cried Downy Duck.
"Watch me swim.
This is fun!"

"Watch me," cried Rusty Turtle.
"Watch me swim.
This is fun!"

"Watch me!" cried Skippy Rabbit.
"Watch me jump over this log."

Cubby Bear said,
"I am not going to run.
I am not going to jump.
I am not going to swim."

What Do You See?

Frisky Squirrel was sitting
on the log.
He was looking into the water.
"I see something," he called.

"Where?" asked Skippy Rabbit.
"Where?" asked Downy Duck.
"Where?" asked Rusty Turtle.
"What?" asked Cubby Bear.

"Look, look!"
cried Frisky Squirrel.

"Oh, I see it!" said Downy Duck.

"I see it, too!" said Rusty Turtle.

"And I see it!"
said Skippy Rabbit.

"Where? What?
What do you see?"
asked Cubby Bear.

He ran to the log.
He ran up and down the log.
He looked all around.

"Where? What?" he cried.
"What do you see?"

"Oh, I see it! I see it!
It is a fish!" cried Cubby Bear.

Splash, splash!
Into the water he went.

"Watch me!" he shouted.
"Watch me eat this fish."

And—
Down went the little fish!

"How he did run!"
laughed Frisky Squirrel.

"How he did jump!"
laughed Skippy Rabbit.

"How he did swim!"
laughed Rusty Turtle and
Downy Duck.

"Ha, ha, ha!" laughed
Cubby Bear.
"How I did eat that fish!
Yum-yum! I like fish!"

I Am Sleepy

"I am sleepy," said Cubby Bear.
"I want to go to sleep.
There is a snug hole
under this big tree.
I will sleep here."

And Cubby Bear went to sleep
in the snug hole
under the big tree.

Frisky Squirrel said,
"I am sleepy, too.
   There is a snug little hole
in the tree.
   I will sleep there."

He ran up the tree
to the snug little hole.

Soon Frisky Squirrel was asleep.
He was asleep in the tree.

Downy Duck sat on the log.

He said, "I am not sleepy.

Oh, I—not—sleepy—

I—not—not."

But Downy Duck was asleep.

Rusty Turtle sat on the log, too.
He looked at Downy Duck.
Downy Duck was asleep.
Rusty Turtle pulled in his head.
He pulled in his feet.
Rusty Turtle was asleep.

Skippy Rabbit sat
under a big leaf.

"I am not sleepy," he said.
"But this is a snug hole.
I will hide under this leaf.
I will hide and I will watch.
I am not sleepy."

He sat very still.
Soon Skippy Rabbit was asleep.

Baby Bear,
Baby Squirrel,
Baby Duck,
Baby Rabbit,
Rusty Turtle—
All were asleep in the woods.

Something Funny

By and by Frisky Squirrel
woke up.

He ran down the tree.

He ran here and there.

He looked all around.

96

He peeped into the hole
under the big tree.
Cubby Bear was asleep.

He peeped under the big leaf.
Skippy Rabbit was asleep.

Frisky Squirrel said,
"Now, that's funny.
I have found Cubby Bear.
I have found Skippy Rabbit.
But I can not find Downy Duck
and Rusty Turtle."

He looked here and there.
He looked up and down.
He looked all around.
He said, "Now, that's funny!
Where can they be?"

Frisky Squirrel ran
to Cubby Bear.

He said, "I can not find
Downy Duck.

I can not find Rusty Turtle.
Where can they be?"

Cubby Bear peeped
from the hole under the big tree.

"I see them," he said.

"They are asleep."

Then Cubby Bear
went to sleep again.

99

Frisky Squirrel ran
to Skippy Rabbit and said,
"I can not find Downy Duck.
I can not find Rusty Turtle.
Where can they be?"

Skippy Rabbit was in the hole
under the big leaf.
He looked out.
"I see them," he said.
"They are asleep."

"Where?" asked Frisky Squirrel.
"Where do you see them?"

Skippy Rabbit wiggled his nose.
He wanted to laugh.
"I see them," he said.
"You see them, too."
He wiggled his nose again.

Frisky Squirrel said,
"I do not see them.
Where are they?"

Downy Duck Has Some Fun

Now Frisky Squirrel was sitting
on a log near Downy Duck
and Rusty Turtle.

But he did not know them.

Soon Downy Duck woke up.
He peeped out at Frisky Squirrel.
"I'll just have some fun," he said.

Downy Duck shouted,
"Quack, quack, quack!
Quack, quack, quack!"

Over went Frisky Squirrel!
Over he went into the water!

Skippy Rabbit wiggled his nose.
Then he hopped up and down
and laughed and laughed.

Frisky Squirrel did not laugh.
He said,
"Downy Duck! Rusty Turtle!
Where were you?"

Downy Duck said,
"I was asleep on the log.
I sleep like this."

Rusty Turtle said,
"I was asleep on the log.
I sleep like this."

"Oh," said Frisky Squirrel.
"Oh, I see! I see!
How funny!"

A Hungry Little Fox

Little Fox had a home
in the woods, too.
He was a hungry little fox.
He wanted to eat little ducks.
He wanted to eat little rabbits.
He wanted to eat little squirrels.

Little Fox was at home.
He was asleep.

By and by Little Fox woke up.

He said, "I wish I had
something to eat.

Where is Mother Fox?

I want her to bring me
some dinner."

But Mother Fox did not come.

Little Fox said, "I can wait.

Mother Fox will be here soon.

She will bring me
something to eat."

Little Fox went to sleep again.

By and by Little Fox
woke up again.

Mother Fox still had not come.

Little Fox said,
"I wish I had a fat little rabbit.
I wish I had a fat little squirrel.
I wish I had a fat little duck.
My! I am hungry!
I could eat them all."

At last Little Fox said,
"I will not wait for Mother Fox.
I can find something to eat.
I can find something good
for my dinner."

Away he went to find his dinner.

Run! Run!

Little Fox looked
for Skippy Rabbit's home.
He could not find it.
He looked
for Frisky Squirrel's home.
He could not find it.

At last Little Fox said,
"I know! I know!
I can find Downy Duck's home.
I will go
to Downy Duck's home.
Yum-yum-yum! I will have
a fat little duck for my dinner!"

He hurried away
to Downy Duck's home.

Skippy Rabbit was in the grass near Downy Duck's home.

He heard something coming.

He sat up and sniffed.

He wiggled his nose.

Then he cried, "I smell a fox! Run! Run fast!"

Frisky Squirrel was in a tree
near Downy Duck's home.

He heard something coming.

And—

He saw Little Fox!

Frisky Squirrel cried,
"Run, run! Run up a tree!"

Rusty Turtle was eating again.

Downy Duck was eating again.

They did not see Little Fox.

They did not smell Little Fox.

They did not hear

Skippy Rabbit cry, "I smell a fox.

Run! Run fast!"

They did not hear

Frisky Squirrel cry,

"Run, run! Run up a tree!"

Little Fox heard Skippy Rabbit.
He heard Frisky Squirrel, too.
He stopped.
He sat very still and looked
at Downy Duck.

"Yum-yum-yum!" he said.
"How I like a fat little duck!
And I am going to have
a fat little duck for my dinner."

Little Fox did not see
Rusty Turtle.

But Rusty Turtle saw Little Fox.
He saw Little Fox looking
at the little duck.

Then—

Little Fox jumped!

He jumped at Downy Duck.

But—

Rusty Turtle snapped!

He snapped at Little Fox.

"My nose! My nose!"
cried Little Fox.

"Oh, my nose!"

And away he ran as fast as
he could go.

"Good-by, Little Fox!"
called Frisky Squirrel.

"Good-by, Little Fox!"
they all called.

Frisky Squirrel and the Nuts

Frisky Squirrel was very happy.
He had found some nuts.
He ran to his snug home
in a hole in a tree.
"I can hide my nuts here,"
he said.

Then he ran down the tree.
He stopped and peeped
into a log.
"I could hide some nuts here,
too," he said.

Up and down, up and down,
went Frisky Squirrel.

He brought some nuts
to his home.

He brought some nuts
to the log.

At last he had all the nuts.

"I wish I could find some more,"
he said.

Then he ran around and around.
He looked here and
he looked there.

Rusty Turtle was going down
to the water.

He saw Frisky Squirrel
coming and going.

Cubby Bear was in the tree.
He saw Frisky Squirrel
coming and going.

Rusty Turtle called,
"Come, Downy Duck!
Come, Skippy Rabbit!
Watch Frisky Squirrel hide
his nuts."

Downy Duck and Skippy Rabbit
said something to Rusty Turtle.
They laughed and laughed.

"I heard you," said Cubby Bear.
And he laughed, too.

At last Frisky Squirrel stopped.

He said, "Now I will have
a good dinner!

Cubby Bear has his fish.

Downy Duck has his worm.

Skippy Rabbit has his grass.

Rusty Turtle has his berries.

But I like nuts.

I will have a good dinner—
a good dinner of nuts.

Yum-yum-yum!"

What! No Nuts!

Up the tree and into the hole
went Frisky Squirrel.

Then out he popped!

He looked all around.

"Now that's funny," he said.

He looked into the hole
again and again.

"That's very funny," he said.

And down the tree he came.

Cubby Bear sat in the tree and
laughed, but Frisky Squirrel
did not see him.

Frisky Squirrel ran as fast as
he could go.
He ran to the log and
peeped into it.

"What! No nuts here!" he cried.
"Oh, oh, oh! I want my nuts!"
He cried and he cried.

"Hello, Cry-baby," called
Cubby Bear.

Frisky Squirrel looked up
into the tree and shouted,
"Did you hide my nuts,
Cubby Bear?"

Downy Duck peeped
over the log.

"Did you hide my nuts,
Downy Duck?"

Rusty Turtle snapped at a bee.

"Did you hide my nuts,
Rusty Turtle?"

Skippy Rabbit wiggled his nose.

"Did you hide my nuts,
Skippy Rabbit?"

Cubby Bear pulled something from a hole in the tree.

Rusty Turtle pulled something from under a leaf.

Downy Duck and Skippy Rabbit pulled something from the log.

Then they called, "Look, Frisky Squirrel, look!"

"Oh, there are my nuts!"
shouted Frisky Squirrel.

"Then you did hide them!
You did! You did! You did!"

"Yes, we did!" they said.
"But we did it just for fun."

"I know," laughed
Frisky Squirrel.

He was happy again, and
they all laughed and laughed.

133

Where Am I?

"I hear something,"
cried Skippy Rabbit.
"I will run away."
And he did run away.

At last he stopped.
He sat very still and
looked all around.

He said, "Where am I?
I do not live here.
I do not know these trees.
I do not live here."

"I'll just run on," he said.
"I'll find my home soon."
And he hurried on.

By and by he stopped again.

"Now that's funny," he said.
"I do not live here.
Where am I?"
Then he ran as fast as
he could go.

Again he stopped.
"Oh, I am lost! I am lost!"
he cried.
And away he ran again.

Mother Rabbit was in the woods.
"Wait, Skippy Rabbit," she called.
"Wait for me!"

Skippy Rabbit was going fast.
He could not stop.
He called to Mother Rabbit,
"I am lost! I am lost!"

At last Skippy Rabbit did stop
"Mother, Mother!" he cried.
"I am lost! I am lost!"

Mother Rabbit said,
"Oh, you funny little rabbit!
You are not lost.
You are with me.
Come, let's go home."

137

Going Home

Skippy Rabbit hopped away
with Mother Rabbit.

"Mother," he asked,
"is Cubby Bear at his home?"

"Yes," said Mother Rabbit.

"Mother," he asked,
"is Downy Duck at his home?"

"Yes," said Mother Rabbit.

Mother Rabbit hopped on.
Skippy Rabbit hopped on.

"Mother," asked Skippy Rabbit,
"is Frisky Squirrel at his home?"

"Yes," said Mother Rabbit.

"Are Downy Duck and
Rusty Turtle at home, too?"
he asked.

"Yes," said Mother Rabbit.

Mother Rabbit hopped on.
Skippy Rabbit hopped on.

"Mother, is Little Fox at home?"
asked Skippy Rabbit.

"Yes," said Mother Rabbit.
"And here is your home,
Baby Rabbit.
Come, you are sleepy!"

"Oh, how good to be at home!"
cried the baby rabbit.

Then he said, "Watch me,
Mother!

Watch me!

Watch me go to sleep!"

Soon Skippy Rabbit
was fast asleep.

WORD LIST

Primer

Watch Me has 136 new words in it. The 62 words of the pre-primer are repeated in the primer.

6 — Watch
Up
go

7 —

8 —

9 — Down
again

10 — he
be

11 — called

12 — in
hole
the

13 —

14 —

15 — Then

16 — Yum-Yum-Yum
smell

17 — sniffed
honey

18 — like

19 — wiggled
his
nose

20 — Help
cried
came

21 — heard
cry

22 — Away
hurried

23 — did

24 — Ha
laughed

25 — My

26 — went
found
honeybee

27 — bee

28 —

29 — Buzz-z-z

30 —

31 —

32 — ran
I'll

33 —

34 — Eating
was
grass

35 — worms
too

36 —

37 — now
big
fat

38 —

39 —

40 —

41 — pulled
at
over

42 — laugh

43 — ate

44 — Cry-Baby
happy
hurt
wanted

45 — Hello

46 — there
saw
Frisky Squirrel

47 — just

48 —

49 —

50 — Picnic
woods
singing

51 —

52 — on

53 — were

54 —

55 — them
Let's
have
56 — Bring
stopped
57 —
58 — some
nuts
59 —
60 — leaf
tablecloth
brought
61 — crack
62 —
63 — sitting
64 — into
65 —
66 —
67 —
68 —
69 —
70 — Out
still
more
71 —
72 — these
By
sleep
73 — head
feet
popped

74 — jumped
shouted
75 — hop
pop
76 — No
77 —
78 — going
Splash
water
79 — log
80 —
81 —
82 —
83 —
84 — looking
85 —
86 —
87 — around
88 — fish
89 — How
that
90 — Sleepy
snug
under
91 — Soon
asleep
92 — sat
93 —
94 — very
95 —

96 — Funny
woke
97 — peeped
98 — that's
find
99 —
100 —
101 —
102 — Has
near
103 —
104 — Quack
105 — hopped
106 —
107 —
108 — had
home
109 — wish
her
dinner
She
110 — could
111 — last
112 — Skippy Rabbit's
Frisky Squirrel's
113 — Downy Duck's
114 — coming
115 —
116 —
117 —

1205